Beautiful Healing

JOURNAL

Lee Felicia Dilbert

BFF
PUBLISHING
HOUSE

Copyright © 2020 BFF Publishing House, LLC

Printed in the United States of America

Website: www.beautifulhealing.life

Email: felicia@beautifulhealing.life

ISBN: 978-1-7352848-3-5

BFF Publishing House is a Limited Liability Corporation dedicated wholly to the appreciation and publication of books for children and adults for the advancement of diversification in literature.

For more information on publishing contact:

Antionette Mutcherson at
bff@bffpublishinghouse.com
Website: bffpublishinghouse.com
Published in the United States by
BFF Publishing House
Tallahassee, Florida First Edition, 2020

This journal belongs to:

_____

Hey Sis,

Your love notes have arrived!

This is your safe space to write your

heart out. Enjoy custom designed

excerpts from Beautiful Healing,

Vol. 1 Seven Love Letters for the

Truth Seeker's Soul.

Say the affirmations out loud.

Then write your own. You got this!

You are worthy.

Love,

Felicia

Excerpt- Beautiful Healing, Vol. 1
Seven Love Letters for the Truth Seeker's Soul
A memoir by Felicia Dilbert

"Sis, I am proud of you. You possess God-given gifts and the world needs to experience them."

@FeliciaDilbert
#BeautifulHealing

love *life* notes

My voice deserves
to be heard

Excerpt- Beautiful Healing, Vol. 1
Seven Love Letters for the Truth Seeker's Soul
A memoir by Felicia Dilbert

"Hope kept me
trudging along through
uncertainty, but then,
I embraced the truth:
the Lord directs my path
and guides me forward."

@FeliciaDilbert
#BeautifulHealing

love *life* notes

I am willing to trust the Lord.

28

Excerpt- Beautiful Healing, Vol. 1
Seven Love Letters for the Truth Seeker's Soul
A memoir by Felicia Dilbert

"I am equipped for the path ahead. I realize that healing occurs over a lifetime and not overnight."

@FeliciaDilbert
#BeautifulHealing

I am not defined by anything that has "happened" to me.

Excerpt- Beautiful Healing, Vol. 1
Seven Love Letters for the Truth Seeker's Soul
A memoir by Felicia Dilbert

"Restoration, I am
coming for you. But
first, I'm pushing the
release button.
I am now choosing to
open the door to my
heart and mind."

@FeliciaDilbert
#BeautifulHealing

love **life** notes

I believe
in myself.

51

Excerpt- Beautiful Healing, Vol. 1
Seven Love Letters for the Truth Seeker's Soul
A memoir by Felicia Dilbert

"Sisters, the word of
God is bigger than
your storm. The Word
has more power than
your feelings."

@FeliciaDilbert
#BeautifulHealing

My life matters.

Excerpt- Beautiful Healing, Vol. 1
Seven Love Letters for the Truth Seeker's Soul
A memoir by Felicia Dilbert

"I am equipped for the path ahead. I realize that healing occurs over a lifetime and not overnight."

@FeliciaDilbert
#BeautifulHealing

love **bR** notes

*Asking for help
is not a bad thing.*

Excerpt- Beautiful Healing, Vol. 1
Seven Love Letters for the Truth Seeker's Soul
A memoir by Felicia Dilbert

"Imagine a path created just
for you that was tailor-made
by the Lord Almighty,
specifically designed with
your feet in mind, leading in a
direction that only you can
walk and arriving at a purpose
that only you can fulfill."

@FeliciaDilbert
#BeautifulHealing

love *her* notes

I am worthy.

Excerpt- Beautiful Healing, Vol. 1
Seven Love Letters for the Truth Seeker's Soul
A memoir by Felicia Dilbert

"When I
experience fear,
I will not fold."

@FeliciaDilbert
#BeautifulHealing

love *bk* notes

I choose to learn from others.

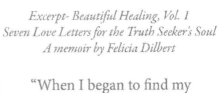

Excerpt- Beautiful Healing, Vol. 1
Seven Love Letters for the Truth Seeker's Soul
A memoir by Felicia Dilbert

"When I began to find my
worth in the Word,
I realized that I am made
in the image of the Lord.
In order to walk out His
truth, I had to believe his
word for myself."

@FeliciaDilbert
#BeautifulHealing

love *life* notes

I am loved.

Excerpt- Beautiful Healing, Vol. 1
Seven Love Letters for the Truth Seeker's Soul
A memoir by Felicia Dilbert

"When a relationship
is valuable, combing
out the knot—the
disagreement—is the
only option."

@FeliciaDilbert
#BeautifulHealing

love *life* notes

I believe
in myself.

Felicia is a writer and creative living in Tallahassee, Florida with her husband. Writing has always been a source of therapy and path of healing for her. Many years later, Felicia's voice and words are being shared poetically in the form of adoration for the Lord and beauty.

Her passion for storytelling and narrative writing are infused with life lessons, tranquility, and building women up through reading, writing, and language.

For more information about Felicia visit
www.beatifulhealing.life

Made in United States
Orlando, FL
03 June 2022

18473239R00072